First Star
The Blue-Pillowed Sky
A Shiny Golden Path
Rainbow Bridge
Slide Down the Sky
From Sea to Shining Sea
Time for Dreams
Across the World
Over the Moon
Sound of the Sea
Promises to Keep

It's a sunny, sunny day today,
There's not a fluffy cloud in the sky.
The sky's all blue in a light blue haze,
The orange sun is shining as it stalks
    along the sea,
And leaves a shiny golden path, for
    me to walk along.

—Sarah Gatti, Age 10

A Shiny Golden Path

An anthology
written and compiled by

Betty Modaressi and **Jan Hirshberg**

Program Authors

Jan Hirshberg
Ann Hughes
S. A. Bernier
Nellie Thomas
Carl Bereiter
Valerie Anderson
Jerome D. Lebo

Open Court
La Salle, Illinois

President and Publisher
M. Blouke Carus

Education Director
Carl Bereiter

Project Coordination
Marsha Roit

Project Planning and Implementation
Thomas G. Anderson,
Commonwealth Strategies, Inc.

Senior Editor
Marilyn F. Cunningham

Permissions
Diane Sikora

Art Direction
Todd Sanders

Cover Design
James Buddenbaum

Acknowledgments

Grateful acknowledgment is given to the following publishers and copyright owners for permission granted to reprint selections from their publications. All possible care has been taken to trace ownership and secure permission for each selection included.

Harper & Row, Publishers, Inc., and William Heinemann Limited: for text and art from "The Garden," from *Frog and Toad Together* by Arnold Lobel, copyright © 1971, 1972 by Arnold Lobel; and for text and art from "The Mouse and the Winds," from *Mouse Tales*, written and illustrated by Arnold Lobel, copyright © 1972 by Arnold Lobel.

Beatrice Schenk de Regniers, for "Keep a Poem in Your Pocket," from *Something Special*; © 1958, renewed 1986 by Beatrice Schenk de Regniers.

Simon & Schuster, Inc., for the poem on p. ii ("It's a Sunny, Sunny Day") by Sarah Gatti, from *Miracles*; copyright © 1966 by Richard Lewis.

Illustration

Victor Ambrus (54–70), Bill and Judie Anderson (1–2), Cheryl Arneman (50–51), Lois Axeman (3–4), Nan Brooks (121), Jim Cummins (75–77), Larry Frederick (45–47), Michael Hague (12–17, 30–41, 48–49, 52–53, 71–74, 79–80), Marika Hahn (82–83), Jan Naimo Jones (9–11), Kees de Kiefte (95–108), Arnold Lobel (84–88, 90–94, 109–120), Diana Magnuson (5–8), Carol Nicklaus (42–44), Barbara Pritzen (122), Sandy Rabinowitz (18–23), Charles Slack (cover), Pat Traub (24–29), Justin Wager (78, 81)

Contents

Little Hills

BETTY MODARESSI

Tip likes to hide his bones in the dirt. He digs big holes and fits a bone into each hole. Tip fills the holes with dirt to hide the bones. The dirt makes a little hill over each bone.

Bill's mother doesn't like Tip's little hills. Each time she sees some little hills of dirt, she cries, "Did Tip dig again? It isn't cute. If he does it one more time, I'll take him in!"

Bill says, "I'll take care of Tip. Tip, don't dig more holes!" Bill's mother smiles. She really does like Tip.

Rick Is Sick

ELIZABETH LANGENDOERFER

"I don't like to be sick," Rick told his mother. "I don't like to sit here alone. Will you please read to me?"

"Yes, I will," said his mother. "First, take this pill and eat some soup. I'll sit here and read to you."

Rick did take his pill. He ate a little soup. And right before Rick was asleep, he heard his mother read, "One time three little pigs told the mother pig they'd like to leave home . . ."

Cold, Pink Drinks

ELIZABETH LANGENDOERFER

"We'll make cold fruit drinks," Linn told Kim. "I'll bring some fruit, and you bring some cubes. Do you think people will pay a dime a drink?"

"Maybe they will," said Kim. "I think people may pay a dime a drink. We'll try it."

So Linn and Kim made cold fruit drinks.
They waited for people to come by and try
the drinks. No one did.

"No one is drinking the fruit drinks,"
cried Linn. "We need to do something."

"We'll tint the drinks pink," said Kim, "and we'll see if people will pay a nickel a drink."

People did pay a nickel a drink, and soon the pink drinks were sold.

8

The Lion Show

BETTY MODARESSI

"It will be time to leave soon," Mr. Smith said to the children. "If we go soon, I think we'll be at the zoo in time to see the lion show. I'll bring the tickets and a picnic. We can find things to drink at the zoo."

At the zoo the lion show was beginning. The lion tamer was working in a ring with six big lions and one little one. She was trying to make the lions leap from stool to stool. The big lions did it. The little lion didn't do a thing the lion tamer told him to do. He was rolling over and over. Each time he rolled over, he kicked his feet in the air.

The lion tamer didn't seem to like the little lion's tricks. The people cheered. They liked the little lion the most.

The Dove and the Ant

AESOP

An ant came to a river to drink. As she drank, she slid into the river and began to sink.

"Save me!" she cried. "Save me!"

A kind dove was standing nearby in the grass. The dove grabbed a twig in her beak and threw the twig into the river.

The ant grabbed the twig and rode it to the riverbank.

Later, the dove was sitting in a tree singing. A man was going to shoot her. The dove didn't see the man aiming at her. The ant did. As the man fired, the ant bit his heel. The man missed, and the dove flew safely away.

The Eagle and the Baker

AESOP

A miller made a trap, and soon a little eagle flew into it. The miller clipped the eagle's wings and tied the eagle to a pole.

The little eagle didn't like to be tied to the pole. It wanted to be free.

One day a kind baker came by and said that he wanted to take the eagle home with

him. The baker paid the miller and gave the eagle a home. The baker was kind to the eagle. He stroked it and patted it. He didn't tie it.

After a few weeks, the eagle's wings grew, and it flew safely away.

Later the eagle came back to see the baker. It gave the baker a fine hare to show that it liked him.

The Tiger and the Kid

AESOP

A kid had strayed away from the bigger goats, to drink. As he drank, a tiger came by. She glanced slyly at the kid and said, "I think I'll eat that nice, fat kid."

"Wait!" said the kid. "I see you have a fancy flute. Please play your flute first, and I'll dance for you."

The tiger liked music, and so she played her flute. The kid pranced and danced.

The owner of the goats heard the flute. He ran after the tiger with a big stick. The tiger had to race away with no dinner.

"After this," said the tiger, "I won't take a chance at being tricked. I'll eat first and play my flute later."

Who's Who?

BETTY MODARESSI

Jean and Joan Jackson are twins, and they are alike. Sometimes they play tricks and try to fool people. Jean likes to make people think she is Joan. Joan likes to make people think she is Jean.

Joan's jacket is blue, and Jean's is green. Sometimes the two sisters trade jackets to try to fool people.

Last Wednesday Jean said, "We can trade jackets and try to fool Mother. She will think that I am you and you are me."

"If you really think that will work, we'll try it," said Joan.

Jean ran home in the blue jacket. Joan wore the green jacket. Mother wasn't fooled. She said, ''Hi, Jean,'' to the girl in the blue jacket and ''Hi, Joan,'' to the one in the green jacket.

"We didn't fool you," said Jean. "What gave the joke away?"

"Your jackets don't say who's who to me," said Mother. "You each do that by the way you act and by the things you do and like."

Mother wiped Jean's face. "Here," she said. "There is a bit of grape jam near your nose. Joan doesn't like grape jam. She likes peach jam. You have a little bag with your jacks in it. Joan doesn't like to play jacks. Joan likes to paint. I can see blue and gold paint beneath her fingernails."

22

Mother smiled at Joan and Jean. "These are only a few of the ways I can see who's who," she said.

"You aren't as alike to me as you are to some people."

Bill's Badger

ELIZABETH LANGENDOERFER

The back field of Bill's farm was flat and
dry. A mother badger had made her home in
a hole there.

One Saturday Bill was playing near the field. The mother badger and two baby badgers ran past him.

Bill ran home fast. He told his dad that he had seen the badgers.

"The badger makes her home in the
back field each year," said Bill's dad. "Don't
go near her. Badgers are mean."

"That's too bad," said Bill. "I wanted to keep one of the babies."

"I'm afraid you can't do that," his dad said. "Badgers can't be tamed. They're wild, and they'll stay wild."

"Can I at least see them?" asked Bill.

"Yes, you can see them from the bridge down the old dirt road," Bill's dad said. "Don't go nearer to them than that."

Each day Bill ran down the road and sat by the bridge.

Bill liked to see the baby badgers grow and play. They grew fast.

"I believe that the little badgers are ready to leave home," said Bill's dad one day. "The mother will leave later. She'll find a new home as soon as winter comes."

"I hope they come back in the spring," Bill replied.

The Wild Pig and the Old Mule

AESOP

One day in June, a wild pig ran over a bridge and came face to face with an old mule. The wild pig began to tease the mule, and soon the mule was mad with rage. The old mule decided to fight the wild pig.

"The mule is weak from old age," said the wild pig. "As the mule is so old, I will be able to win a fight with him. I will have to stay away from his huge teeth, so I can attack him from behind."

The wild pig ran at the mule. As he did, the old mule threw back his heels and kicked the wild pig right in the face. The wild pig flew into the air and landed in the grass near the bridge. He raced over the bridge and ran away fast. As he ran away, the wild pig said, "After this, if I have to fight an old mule, I will think of both the bite and the kick."

The Wolf and the Kids

JACOB and WILHELM GRIMM

A mother goat had to go away from home to find some food. She had to leave her kids at home. "Stay inside and keep the door locked," she said to her kids. "The wolf may be near. He likes to eat kids. If he

comes here, he'll try to eat you. Do not open the door till you hear me tap."

One of the kids said, "The wolf might tap too."

"Dear me! You are right," said the mother goat. "We will have to have a signal. I will say, 'The wolf is bad.' Do not open the door till you hear me say that."

The mother goat trotted away.

The wolf was hiding nearby, and he heard the mother goat. He licked his chops and ran over to the goats' home. He tapped at the door.

One of the kids said, "Is it my mother, or is it the wolf?"

"Your mother," said the wolf.

"Give me the signal," said the kid.

The wolf smiled slyly and said, "The wolf is bad."

The kid stopped to think.

At last he said, "Are you really my mother? If so, go to the window and show me your beard."

The wolf did not have a beard to show the kid, so he trotted sadly away to his home.

The Donkey in the Lion's Skin

AESOP

A lion's skin was lying on the grass. A silly donkey got into it. "I will hide in this skin," said the donkey. "I will use it to scare the ox, the deer, and the tiger. They will see the skin and think that I am a mean lion."

The donkey ran at the ox. "A lion is after me," screamed the ox. "The lion is mean. It will kill me and eat me!" The ox trotted away fast.

The donkey ran at the deer. "A lion! A lion!" cried the deer. "The lion will kill me!" The deer raced away and hid behind a tree.

The donkey ran at the tiger. "A lion is after me!" said the tiger. "The lion is bigger and meaner than I am. I cannot fight it and win." The tiger backed away and ran.

"I'm a fine lion," said the donkey. "I think I can roar like a lion too. If I roar, I will be more like a lion."

Soon the donkey came to a fox. "I will roar at that fox," said the donkey. "That will really scare him." The donkey ran at the fox, braying. The fox stopped and sat down. He stared at the donkey.

"Aren't you afraid of me?" asked the donkey.

"No, I'm not," said the fox. "You are not a real lion. Real lions roar. They don't bray."

The Magic Show

ELIZABETH LANGENDOERFER

The people sat still as the man in the cape and high silk hat ran to the center of the stage. He held a magic wand in his hand. The man waved his magic wand, and smoke rose from a huge glass bowl on the table. The people clapped and cheered.

Next, the man reached into his hat and grabbed a little rabbit. He waved his magic wand, and the rabbit became a pretty dove in a fancy, golden cage. The people gasped!

One more time the man waved the magic wand. This time the dove flew away, and the cage vanished. The people cheered! They asked to see more magic tricks. They did see one more magic trick. The man raised his left hand high in the air. He waved the magic wand with his right hand. Smoke rose from near his feet, and he vanished from sight. The magic show was over. It was time to go home.

Not Really Magic

B. ADKINS

Some tricks that seem to be magic really aren't. You can make people think that you are going to do a magic trick and surprise them by doing a trick that isn't really magic.

To get ready to do the trick, hold a sheet of paper in your left hand. Hold a little box in your right hand. Say, "This is magic paper.

I can make this paper hold this heavy box in the air." Let a few people try to hold the box in the air on the paper. They will find that the paper is too weak to hold the box.

Spread the sheet of paper on the table.
Then fold it to make little pleats like those in a
paper fan. Stand the paper on its edge on
the table and set the box on it.

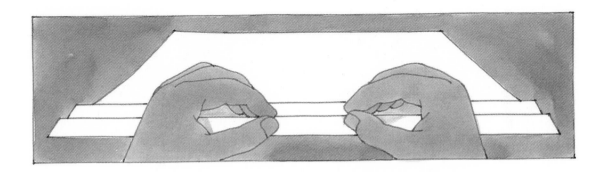

The people will see
the sheet of paper
holding the box in the
air over the table.

The Goose That Laid the Golden Eggs

AESOP

One day a plump goose laid a golden egg. The man who owned the goose was very happy.

Each day after that, she laid one golden egg.

"Soon I shall be rich," said the man.

But the man was a greedy person.

"This goose must be stuffed with gold," he said. "I must catch the goose and cut her open to see." That is just what he did.

But there was no gold inside the goose. The goose was just a plain goose inside.

The man scratched his head and said, "What a fool I am! I have killed the goose that laid the golden eggs."

Up, Up and Away

BETTY MODARESSI

On a breezy day
My kite goes
Up, up and away.

On a stormy day
My kite comes
Down, down to stay.

The Crow and the Pitcher

AESOP

One day right after breakfast, a thirsty crow came to a pitcher of water and tried to get a drink. She was sad to find that she wasn't able to drink. The water was too low in the pitcher. The crow's beak did not reach the water, and her head did not fit into the top of the pitcher. She sat on some pebbles in a ditch to think.

Then she lifted a pebble in her beak and dropped it into the pitcher. She fetched more and more pebbles and dropped them into the pitcher. The water rose higher and higher. At last the water reached the top of the pitcher, and the thirsty crow drank her fill.

The Three Little Pigs

AN ENGLISH TALE

[Part 1]

Once upon a time three little pigs lived with a mother pig in a little house. One day the mother pig said, ''Four of us can't live in this house. It is much too little. You must go and make your own houses.''

So the three little pigs left home. After a while they met a man with a load of straw.

The first little pig said, "Please, Mister, sell me your straw."

"Why do you want this straw?" the man asked.

"I want to make a house with it," said the little pig. "It will be easy to make a straw house. I can make my house fast. Then I can play."

"I don't think this load of straw is right for you," said the man. "Your house will be weak. But take the straw if you really want it."

The first little pig made his house of straw. Then he played.

Meanwhile, the second little pig met a man with a load of sticks. "Please sell me your sticks, Mister," said the little pig.

"Why do you want these sticks?" the man asked.

"I want to make a house with them," said the little pig. "I don't like to work. A stick house will be easy to make. After I make my house, I'll have lots of time to sleep."

58

"Your house will be weak," said the man, "but take the sticks if you want them."

The second little pig made his house of sticks. Then he slept.

The third little pig hummed a tune as he walked on alone down the road. After a while he met a man with a load of bricks. "Please, Mister, sell me your bricks," said the little pig.

"Why do you want these bricks?" the man asked.

"I want to use them to make a house," said the little pig. "I want a house that will stand up when the wind blows. I want my house to keep me dry when it rains. It will be a lot of work to make a brick house, but I don't mind."

"You can make a fine house with these bricks," said the man. "Take them."

So the third little pig made his house of bricks.

[Part 2]

Soon a big, bad wolf came up to the straw house. He rapped on the door and said, "Little pig, little pig, let me come in!"

"No!" replied the little pig. "Not by the hair of my chinny-chin-chin will I let you come in."

63

"Then I'll huff, and I'll puff, and I'll blow your house in!" said the wolf.

So he huffed, and he puffed, and he blew the weak straw house in. He ate the little pig.

A while later the big, bad wolf came to the house made of sticks. When he got to the door, he rapped on it and said, "Little pig, little pig, let me come in."

"No! No!" replied the second little pig. "Not by the hair of my chinny-chin-chin will I let you come in!"

65

"Then I'll huff, and I'll puff, and I'll blow your house in!" said the wolf.

So he huffed, and he puffed, and he blew the weak stick house in. He ate the second little pig.

The next day the big, bad wolf came to the house made of bricks. He rapped on the door and said, "Little pig, little pig, let me come in."

"No! No! No!" replied the third little pig. "Not by the hair of my chinny-chin-chin will I let you come in!"

"Then I'll huff, and I'll puff, and I'll blow your house in," said the wolf.

So he huffed, and he puffed. He puffed and he huffed. Then he huffed, and he puffed some more. But he did not blow the brick house in.

"I'll get that little pig," the wolf whispered to himself. "I'll get up on top of the house and go down the chimney."

It was nearly time for supper. The third little pig had placed a big pot over the fire in the fireplace just below the chimney. He wanted to make stew for supper.

Down the chimney came the wolf! He landed right in the pot. The little pig slapped the lid on the pot. Soon he had wolf stew for his supper.

The third little pig lived happily in his brick house for the rest of his life.

The Mice and the Cat

AESOP

Quite some time ago a family of mice lived in an old house. A big, mean cat lived in the same house. The cat was quiet and quick. She sneaked up on the mice and killed lots of them. The mice were not able to hear her and get away.

One day the mice had a meeting. The leader was a wise, old grandmother. When it was her turn to speak, she said, "What can we do to make the cat quit killing us? We must quickly think of a plan."

One of the mice spoke up. "Let's tie a bell to the cat's neck," he said. "When we hear the bell, we can quickly run away."

Most of the mice cheered when they heard the plan.

"That seems to be a fine plan," said the old grandmother, "but some things are more easily said than done. Tell me one thing. Who will tie the bell to the cat's neck?"

Not one of the mice spoke.

"I see what you mean," said one of the little mice. "It is easy to say that we will tie a bell to the cat, but it is not so easy to do it."

Camping

ELIZABETH LANGENDOERFER

"Wake up, Mom," whispered Antonio. "Did you hear what I heard?"

"I didn't hear a thing," said Mom. "I was fast asleep."

"Something is near the tent," said Antonio. "I heard it. Do you think it's a wolf or a wildcat?"

"Did you hear a howl or a growl?" asked Mom.

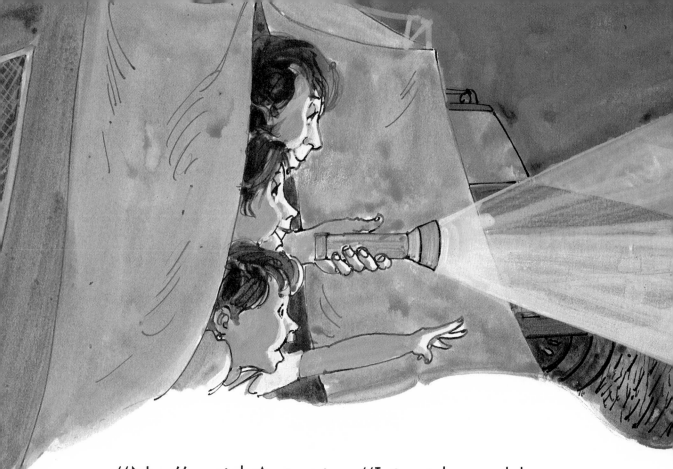

"No," said Antonio, "I just heard leaves
cracking and twigs snapping."

"Let's wake Dad up now," said Mom.
"Then we'll see if something is there."

Soon Dad got the flashlight and opened
the tent flap. The light shone on a big, brown
thing between the tent and the truck.

Then Antonio heard something else.

"Moo!"

"Wow!" said Antonio. "It's only a big, brown cow. I'm not afraid of a cow."

Antonio got back into his sleeping bag. "I think I'll like camping," he said. "I don't mind cows—but I hope we never hear howls and growls at night."

The Purple Cow

GELETT BURGESS

I never saw a Purple Cow,
    I never hope to see one;
But I can tell you, anyhow,
    I'd rather see than be one.

The Hare and the Hound

AESOP

A brown-and-white hound found a hare eating grass near the fence. The hound chased the hare in and out and around the fence. It chased the hare up and down hills. In about an hour the hound was out of breath. He gave up the chase and went home.

"What a poor runner you are!" said the hound's mistress. "You didn't outrun the hare."

"It wasn't a real race," said the hound. "The hare was running to save its life. I was only running to catch my dinner."

I've Got a Dog

ANONYMOUS

I've got a dog as thin as a rail;
He's got fleas all over his tail.
Every time his tail goes flop,
The fleas on the bottom all hop
to the top.

Keep a Poem in Your Pocket

BEATRICE SCHENK DE REGNIERS

Keep a poem in your pocket
and a picture in your head
and you'll never feel lonely
at night when you're in bed.

The little poem will sing to you
the little picture bring to you
a dozen dreams to dance to you
at night when you're in bed.

So—
Keep a picture in your pocket
and a poem in your head
and you'll never feel lonely
at night when you're in bed.

The Garden

ARNOLD LOBEL

[Part 1]

Frog was in his garden.
Toad came walking by.
"What a fine garden
you have, Frog," he said.

"Yes," said Frog. "It is very nice,
but it was hard work."
"I wish I had a garden," said Toad.
"Here are some flower seeds.
Plant them in the ground," said Frog,
"and soon you will have a garden."
"How soon?" asked Toad.

"Quite soon," said Frog.
Toad ran home.
He planted the
        flower seeds.

"Now seeds," said Toad,

"start growing."

Toad walked up and down

a few times.

The seeds did not start to grow.

Toad put his head

close to the ground

and said loudly,

"Now seeds, start growing!"

Toad looked at the

ground again.

The seeds did not start

to grow.

Toad put his head
very close to the ground and shouted,
"NOW SEEDS, START GROWING!"

Frog came running up the path.
"What is all this noise?" he asked.
"My seeds will not grow," said Toad.

"You are shouting too much,"
said Frog. "These poor seeds are afraid
to grow."
"My seeds are afraid to grow?"
asked Toad.

"Of course," said Frog.

"Leave them alone for a few days.

Let the sun shine on them, and

let the rain fall on them.

Soon your seeds will start to grow."

That night

Toad looked out of his window.

"Drat!" said Toad.

"My seeds have not

started to grow.

They must be afraid of the dark."

Toad went out to his garden

with some candles.

"I will read the seeds a story,"

said Toad.

"Then they will not be afraid."

Toad read a long story
to his seeds.

[Part 2]

All the next day
Toad sang songs
to his seeds.

And all the next day
Toad read poems
to his seeds.

And all the next day
Toad played music
for his seeds.
Toad looked at the ground.
The seeds still did not
start to grow.

"What shall I do?" cried Toad.
"These must be
the most frightened seeds
in the whole world!"

Then Toad felt very tired,
and he fell asleep.
"Toad, Toad, wake up," said Frog.
"Look at your garden!"

Toad looked
at his garden.
Little green plants
were coming up
out of the ground.

"At last," shouted Toad,
"my seeds have stopped
being afraid to grow!"
"And now you will have
a nice garden too," said Frog.
"Yes," said Toad,
"but you were right, Frog.
It was very hard work."

The Little Red Hen

AN ENGLISH TALE

[Part 1]

One day a little red hen was strolling down a path. She found a little sack on the ground. She picked up the sack and found that it was filled with seeds. The seeds were grains of wheat.

"I can't do much with this little sack of wheat," said the little red hen. "But if I plant the seeds, much more wheat will grow. Then I will have quite a lot of wheat." So the little red hen went home with the sack of wheat.

"I will need some help to plant the wheat," said the little red hen. She went to the cat, the dog, and the pig.

"Who will help me plant some wheat?" asked the little red hen.

"Not I," said the cat.

"Not I," said the dog.

"Not I," said the pig.

"Then I will have to plant the wheat myself," said the little red hen. And she did.

Soon the wheat was growing, but the weeds were growing too. "Now the wheat needs to be hoed, and the weeds must be cut down," said the little red hen. She went to get some help.

"Who will help me hoe the wheat?"
asked the little red hen.

"Not I," said the cat.

"Not I," said the dog.

"Not I," said the pig.

"Then I will have to hoe the wheat
myself," said the little red hen. And she did.

The wheat grew, and soon it was ripe
and ready to be cut. The little red hen said,
"It is time to cut the wheat now." She went to
get some help.

"Who will help me cut the wheat?"
asked the little red hen.

"Not I," said the cat.

"Not I," said the dog.

"Not I," said the pig.

"Then I will have to cut the wheat
myself," said the little red hen. And she did.

[Part 2]

After the wheat was cut, the little red hen said, "Now the wheat must be ground into flour." She went to get some help.

"Who will help me grind the wheat?"
asked the little red hen.

"Not I," said the cat.
"Not I," said the dog.
"Not I," said the pig.
"Then I will have to grind the wheat
myself," said the little red hen. And she did.

When the little red hen got home with the flour, she said, "Now I will use this flour to bake some bread." She asked for help.

"Who will help me bake some bread?" asked the little red hen.

"Not I," said the cat.

"Not I," said the dog.

"Not I," said the pig.

"Then I will have to bake the bread myself," said the little red hen. And she did.

Soon the bread was baked and ready to
eat. The little red hen asked, "Who will help
me eat the bread?"

"I will," said the cat.

"I will," said the dog.

"I will," said the pig.

"No," said the little red hen. "When I found the wheat seeds, I asked you to help me, but you didn't. You didn't help me plant the wheat. You didn't help me hoe the wheat. You didn't help me cut the wheat. You didn't help me grind the wheat into flour. You didn't even help me bake the bread. Now you won't help me eat the bread. I will eat the bread myself, and I will share it with my little chicks." And that is just what the little red hen did.

The Mouse and the Winds

ARNOLD LOBEL

A mouse went out in his boat, but there was no wind. The boat did not move.

"Wind!" shouted the mouse. "Come down and blow my boat across this lake!"

"Here I am," said the west wind.

The west wind blew and blew. The mouse and the boat went up in the air . . .

and landed on the roof of a house.

"Wind!" shouted the mouse. "Come down and blow my boat off this house!"

"Here I am," said the east wind.
The east wind blew and blew.

The mouse and the boat and the house went
up into the air . . .

and landed on the top of a tree.

"Wind!" shouted the mouse. "Come down and blow my boat off this house and off this tree!"

"Here I am," said the south wind.

The south wind blew and blew. The mouse and the boat and the house and the tree went up into the air . . .

and landed on the top of a mountain.

"Wind!" shouted the mouse. "Come down and blow my boat off this house and off this tree and off this mountain!"

"Here I am," said the north wind.

The north wind blew and blew. The
mouse and the boat and the house and the
tree and the mountain went up in the
air . . . and came down into the lake.

The mountain sank and became an island. The tree landed on the island and burst into bloom.

The house landed next to the tree.

A lady looked out of a window in the
house and said, "What a nice place to live!"

And the mouse just sailed away.

Blow, Wind, Blow

MOTHER GOOSE

Blow, wind, blow! And go, mill, go!
That the miller may grind his corn;
That the baker may take it,
And into rolls make it,
And send us some hot in the morn.

Rain

ROBERT LOUIS STEVENSON

The rain is raining all around,
  It falls on field and tree,
It rains on the umbrellas here,
  And on the ships at sea.